Red Riding H

by Nick Cornall
edited by Alison Hedger

The pantomime story of Little Red Riding Hood
with 6 new songs

Duration approx. 50 minutes

For Primary school children with mixed abilities

The main character parts suit KEY STAGE 2
Younger children join the choir and dancers, dressed as
woodland animals, trees or country folk

TEACHER'S BOOK
Piano score complete with vocal line and chord symbols
plus production notes. Add percussion and sound effects as desired

---

SONGS

1.	Get Your Best Smile Out	*All*
2.	Tiddley Om Pom Pom	*All*
3.	I Don't Want To Be The Bad Wolf Any More	*William + All*
4.	Trying To Make Crime Pay	*Robbers + All*
5.	Turaluralu	*All*
6.	It's That Kind Of Christmas Time Of The Year	*All*

Incidental music is included

The PUPIL'S BOOK contains the play and song words
Order No. GA10992

A matching tape cassette of the music for rehearsals and performances is also available,
Order No. GA10993, side A with vocals included and side B with vocals omitted.

© Copyright 1995 Golden Apple Productions
A division of Chester Music Limited
8/9 Frith Street, London W1V 5TZ

Order No. GA10991

ISBN 0-7119-5026-1

In RED RIDING HOOD Nick Cornall retells the traditional story of Little Red Riding Hood giving it some very innovative twists, making this a delightful pantomime for children to perform. Granny is not the sweet little old lady we are used to and William Wolf is a round peg in a square hole and really quite nice. However, BB Wolf is moving into the area, and is exactly as nasty as a wicked wolf should be! The traditional "what big eyes you have" routine is included.

This version of RED RIDING HOOD has Syble the Squirrel (a woodland pet of Red Riding Hood) and two bungling burglars, Knuckler and Fingers who are out to do their worst. Also included is the traditional Woodman. However, no one had reckoned on Granny Hood being out of character! "All's well that ends well" — and all ends well. Or does it?

PRODUCTION NOTES

All: Gr. 2 dancers & percussion
Some: Gr. 3 actors (exploratory)
Some: Gr. 4 & 5 narrators

or

Gr. 5 Actors (exploratory)
Gr. 3 & 4 narrators
Gr. 2 dancers & percussion.

CHARACTERS

Can have up to 18

Narrator 1
Narrator 2
Kathryn 5B
Red Riding Hood — Nura & Alistair 5B 5BA
Could be 2 if necessary *Syble* — *Syble the Squirrel*   a woodland pet
Mother — *Maria 5BA*   Mrs Hood
Woodman *Erika 5BS*   Red Riding Hood's father
William Wolf — *Miren 5B*   quite nice really
Humorous — Knuckler *— Michael 5BA*
Fingers *— Sheela 5B*   two dastardly robbers
Granny Hood *Maya 5B* more the witch of the wood rather than a helpless old lady
Humorous — BB Wolf *Aiko 5BA*   a genuine big bad wolf
Foxy — *Koichiro 5B*   assistant to BB Wolf
Choir   provide the songs and action/dance routines, also speak in unison at places marked **All**

✳ = lots to say   O = little to say
* indicates solo singing
No Solos

Everyone sings songs: 1, 3, 4 & 6
Choir sing songs: 2 & 5

SEVEN SCENES INVOLVING THREE SETS

1.	Woodman's Cottage	Red Riding Hood has to take some food to Granny.
2.	In The Woods	Red Riding Hood and Syble the Squirrel meet William Wolf. Introducing Knuckler and Fingers.
3.	Granny's Cottage	The robbers tie Granny up.
4.	In The Woods	BB Wolf and Foxy move into the area and meet Red Riding Hood, the Robbers, William and Syble.
5.	Woodman's Cottage	William and Syble alert the Woodman.
6.	In The Woods	The robbers and heroes meet.
7.	Granny's Cottage	Resolution of the plot. Granny casts her spell and everyone lives happily ever after. However this may depend upon Granny . . .

PRINCIPAL PROPS

axe
basket filled with food
soup flask
large book — PICTURES FROM THE ZOO
black swag bag
rope
gag
lace cap, shawl, glasses
rocking chair

STAGING AND SETS

The choir plays a very important part in RED RIDING HOOD and should be facing the audience. This body of singers also provides the performers for the action/dance routines. Whole classes can be involved in the dance sequences and gives the very youngest members of the production an opportunity to take the stage. The choir can be woodland animals, trees or country folk dressed in bright simple tunics. They provide a colourful and enchanting visual backdrop to the action.

The three sets can be more imaginary than real, but the children will love designing Granny's gingerbread cottage with its candy drains, sugar rock lintel and candyfloss wood smoke: "the whole point is you can eat it bit by bit".

COSTUMES

The main characters are dressed as one would expect. Refer to any illustrated book of the title Red Riding Hood.

STAGE DIRECTIONS

These have been kept to the minimum. The actions, gestures, entries and exits will be self-evident from the story. Just act out the dialogue taking care to speak slowly enough so that the audience can catch the rhymes and story line.

MUSIC AND DANCE

Please embellish the music as desired. A simple piano part is given. Add percussion if available, not forgetting the noises which always add extra humour to a pantomime. A sound source for Granny's spell is needed. This can be electronic or something as simple as a Swannee whistle. The dances can be simple skipping in a circle or something more complicated creating floor patterns and incorporating clapping. You may even be lucky enough to have some volunteer ballet dancers, but dress them in keeping with the pantomime.

CASSETTE TAPE

A matching tape of the music (GA10993) may help you with learning the songs and will be very useful if you are taking rehearsals single-handed. The B side has no vocal tracks and so can be used for performances.

A RECOMMENDATION FROM NICK CORNALL

If at all possible involve parents in your production getting them to sing along with the songs. A couple of rehearsals would be ample. The enjoyment of parents and friends sharing in their children's production creates an invaluable community spirit which will be long remembered by everyone.

(Throughout your production you may need more music for exits and links. Play the music from the previous song, and try playing up an octave which can make a pleasant musical change.)

BACKGROUND NOTES ON LITTLE RED RIDING HOOD

The story of Little Red Riding Hood is known throughout Europe and follows the Germanic tradition of a saviour huntsman (here called the woodman) who kills the wolf, although some believe the story has its origins in Italy. In France the story is called "Le Petit Chaperon Rouge". The fact that the heroine is dressed in red may have no more significance than that it is one of the first colours loved by young children.

Red Riding Hood is not strictly a fairy story as these include diminutive supernatural beings who have their own kingdom. Many of the European fairy stories originate from the East, being brought to Europe at the time of the Crusades. However, the term fairy story now encompasses a wider field and includes stories such as Cinderella and Jack and the Beanstalk, where a character who is almost always young, encounters strange and magical events. This interpretation is not found earlier than the eighteenth century.

A myth, from the Greek 'mythos' meaning word, saying or story, is a symbolic narrative reflecting society and culture. In the West these include fables, sagas, legends and epic tales.

Whereas myths and fairy stories are about humble humans who meet and overcome adversaries such as ogres, giants, witches and wicked relations (jealous stepmothers, sisters etc.) the folktale plays more upon the relation of man to animals. Traditional plots include lone travellers, a fear of the wolf, a forest (dangerous location), a quest to overcome evil and a heroine to be saved.

A folktale is a simple story which reflects social situations and depicts the hopes and fears of ordinary folk. The origins of the folktale or folklore can be traced back to the late eighteenth century, although many suppose that the origins go back much further.

The story of RED RIDING HOOD is a folktale at its best and Nick Cornall's innovative twists to the story have done nothing to damage this concept. He has grafted onto the story some appealing Pantomime ideas, making this a sparkling Christmas show for children to perform which is characterised by humour, farce, corny jokes, outlandish doggerel and catchy music.

Alison Hedger

1. GET YOUR BEST SMILE OUT

All

Glockenspiels
2 students per glockenspiel
(4 glocks/8 students)
+ triangles or
maracas?

Terry - triangle
Kris - maracas
Haji - triangle

All others playing
glockenspiel.

With enthusiasm ♩ = 126

(repeat as necessary)

1. Get your best smile out from un-der the stair.
3. And that's some-thing we know we can all share.
5. Can't you hear that mag-ic note in the air?

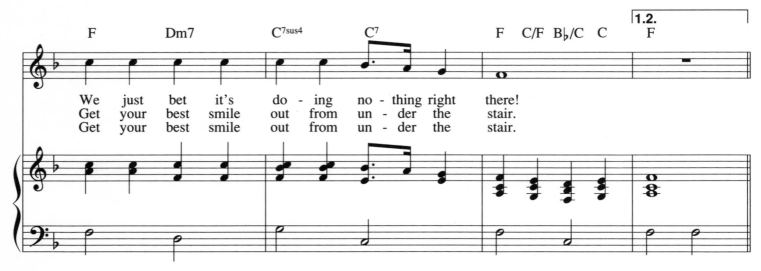

We just bet it's do-ing no-thing right there!
Get your best smile out from un-der the stair.
Get your best smile out from un-der the stair.

(this bar after verse 5, and on to verse 6 below)

2. Put your heart on your sleeve, close your
4. Put some hap - pi - ness on, soon your

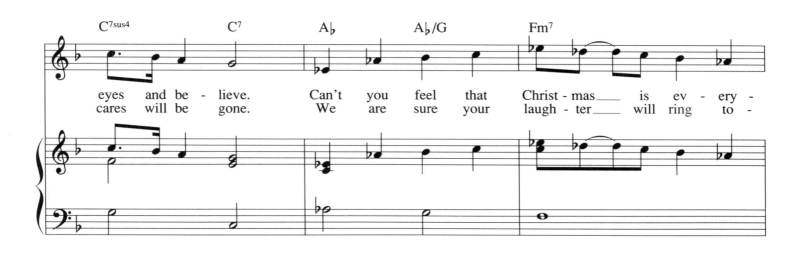

eyes and be - lieve. Can't you feel that Christ - mas____ is ev - ery -
cares will be gone. We are sure your laugh - ter____ will ring to -

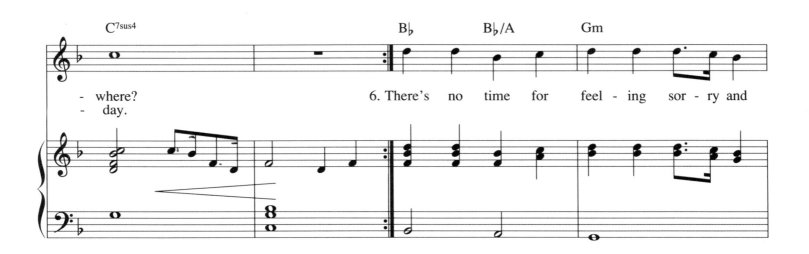

- where?
- day.

6. There's no time for feel - ing sor - ry and

frown - ing all day through. What we need's a hap - py sto - ry to

ban - ish the blues. 7. Get your best smile out from un - der the

stair. We just bet it's do - ing no - thing right

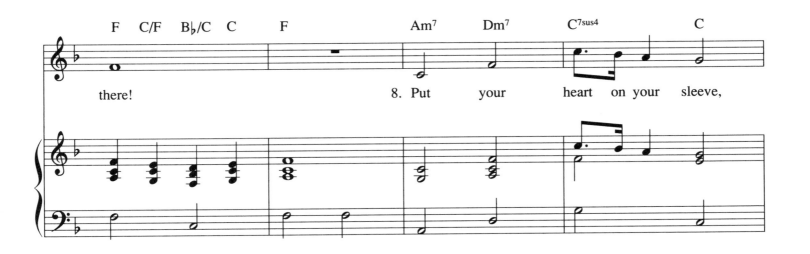

there!   8. Put   your   heart   on your   sleeve,

close   your   eyes and be - lieve.   Can't you feel that   Christ - mas___ is ev - ery -

- where?   9. And   that's some - thing   we   know   we   can all

share.   Get your best smile out from un - der the

stair.   10. Go and look up in the loft,

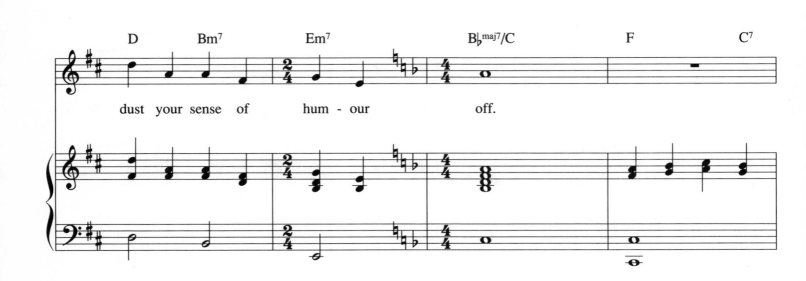

dust your sense of hum - our off.

Red Riding Hood

by Nick Cornall
edited by Alison Hedger

The pantomime story of Little Red Riding Hood
with 6 new songs

for Primary school children

Handwritten annotations in left margin:

2S instruments
Emmy finger cymbals
Joey finger cymbals
Klaus   "   "
Makoto   "   "
Nicola claves
Hiro claves
Mark maraca
Shun Kokiriko

Exploratory instruments:
Kris maracas
Terry triangle
Hoji triangle
Erica finger cymbals
Saki
Remmy
Toby
Kmira   } 4 metalophones
Lisa M
Jonathan
Lisa T.
Jessica

Pupil's Book
Contains the play and song words

The Teachers Book, Order No. GA10991 contains the piano score with the vocal line,
chord symbols and production notes

A matching tape cassette of the music for rehearsals and performances is also available,
Order No. GA10993, side A with vocals included and side B with vocals omitted

Order No. GA10992

ISBN 0-7119-5027-X

OPENING SONG

Instrumentalists on stage.

1.

GET YOUR BEST SMILE OUT

All

1. Get your best smile out from under the stair.
    We just bet it's doing nothing right there!

2. Put your heart on your sleeve,
    Close your eyes and believe.
    Can't you feel that Christmas is everywhere?

3. And that's something we know we can all share.
    Get your best smile out from under the stair.

4. Put some happiness on,
    Soon your cares will be gone.
    We are sure your laughter will ring today.

5. Can't you hear that magic note in the air?
    Get your best smile out from under the stair.

6. There's no time for feeling sorry and frowning all day through.
    What we need's a happy story to banish the blues.

7. Get your best smile out from under the stair.
    We just bet it's doing nothing right there!

8. Put your heart on your sleeve,
    Close your eyes and believe.
    Can't you feel that Christmas is everywhere?

9. And that's something we know we can all share.
    Get your best smile out from under the stair.

10. Go and look up in the loft,
    Dust your sense of humour off.

11. Get your best smile out from under the,
    Get your best smile out from under the,
    Get your best smile out from under the stair.

SCENE 1   WOODMAN'S COTTAGE

Narrator 1

Lauren K. & Emiri 4P
Non-choir   1

Welcome everybody to another pantomime.
Another year of 'iffy' songs and rather rotten rhyme.
We're in the woods again, you'll note.
The same old twigs and sticks.
This tree's been in it every year, since 1976.

Narrator 2

Elly & Kay 4P
Non-choir   2

They all live 'round here you know.
There's Mother Goose and Jack,
Cinderella; she's up at 'Dunskivvying' *at the ball*
With her coach, parked round the back.

Miria & Harumi 4P
Non-choir   3

The Three Little Pigs, they live here,
Or one of them that is.
Two of them didn't quite make it!
Still, that's pantomime show biz.

Narrator 1

Yurica & Illi 4P
Non-choir   4

Fairy godmothers, witches, elves,
Wizards on the make.
And half the crowned heads of Europe *from around the world*
On lily pads, down by the lake!

Narrator 2

Erica 4P
Non-choir   5

But this story's a bit on the quiet,
Nothing much goes on.
A quaint and simple story line.

All

Of course, we could be wrong.

Red Riding Hood

and Gyble
Syble, ~~Syble~~, where are you?
You naughty squirrel you.
We really must be going in,
It's nearly half past two.

Syble

Here ~~I am~~ *We are*, Red Riding Hood.
And less of the "Syble" please.
You've no idea how the other squirrels
Like to taunt and tease.

'Scavenger of the Forest', that's ~~my~~ *our* name.
We're ~~I'm~~ mean and cool and tough.
Not something you get in the shops
All big brown eyes and fluff.

Red Riding Hood

But "Syble" ~~is~~ *and Syble are* just right for you,
A name that really suits.
You're all squidgy and cuddly and . . . .

Syble

Oh no, she's going to call ~~me~~ *us* "cute."

Mother

Red Riding Hood, Red Riding Hood.
Oh there you are, now see,
Your father will be home.
We have to get his tea.

Red Riding Hood

Coming mother, shan't be long.
I'll bring some wood in too.
What are we having for dinner then?

Mother

I thought of squirrel stew.

Syble

She doesn't like ~~me~~ *us* much, does she?
Neither does your dad.

Red Riding Hood

Oh, she's only making fun.
They're really not that bad.

Syble

What does your dad do exactly?
I'm sure he does it nicely.
But what does being a woodman involve
I mean what is a woodman, precisely?

Red Riding Hood

I dunno, he goes out 'wooding' I suppose,
I've never really asked.
He just goes off with his great big axe
And mummy packs a flask.

4

Syble It's not as though we're short of wood,
I mean, just take a look around.
Wouldn't he be better selling fancy goods
Or getting a paper round?

Mother Are you going to stand there
With that smelly squirrel all day? *(those)*
Or are you going to do some work?
Your father will be on his way.

Red Riding Hood I'd best go, she's in a mood,
I'd really better hurry.

Syble *We'll* I'll see you in the forest later.

Red Riding Hood She'll cheer up, don't worry. Bye.

(Syble exits)

Woodman Hello there, child, who was that?
Those That squirrel again I bet.
They're She's rather smelly and old you know.
Can't you get a proper pet?

Red Riding Hood Hello father dear,
Oh Syble's rather sweet. *(& Syble)*
They don't She doesn't smell an awful lot
It's mainly just her feet. *(their)*

Woodman I'm home dear, what's for tea?
(calling to Mother) I'm tired and starving too.
I could eat up anything . . .
Aside . . . (As long as it isn't stew).

Mother It's stew.

Woodman Oh, that's nice dear.

Now little Red, before my tea
I have a little task.
Go and get some of that lovely stew
And put it in a flask.

Red Riding Hood Oh no dad! You're sending me
To visit Granny Hood.

Woodman   You know she's old and very poor
              We have to send her food.

Red Riding Hood   "Old and very poor" indeed!
                       You know she's very rich.
                       Granny Hood, it's very well known,
                       Is a most successful witch.

Woodman   Sh! Not too loud, for heaven's sake,
              Do you want someone to hear?
              Witches aren't very popular,
              Especially 'round here.

Red Riding Hood   I'm not surprised, think of the neighbours.
                       Snow White, Hansel and Gretel.
                       They're rather suspicious of old ladies who use
                       A cauldron for a kettle.

Woodman   Look, get a basket from your mum,
              With lots of food to tempt her.
              And don't worry about Granny Hood,
              She's just got a bit of a temper.

(Red Riding Hood exits)

Woodman   She's alright really, is Granny Hood,
              Just a bit strange in the head.
              She's just got the one cauldron and a cat
              And cottage made of gingerbread.

(Red Riding Hood enters with basket)

Red Riding Hood   Well, I'll be off father, quick as I can,
                       Off to Granny's place.
                       I've got stew, bread, butter, cheese,
                       Oh! and garlic, just in case.

Woodman   Right, and mind the wolf!

Red Riding Hood   What, William? He's a big softy really!

Woodman   That girl!

choir! Tiddley Om Pom Pom

⚹ 2H on stage 6

2. **TIDDLEY OM POM POM**

All sing with action routine/dance

1. If you are feeling lonely, if you are down,
   If all the skies are turning grey,
   Just make a little happy kind of a sound,
   All of your cares will fly away.

Refrain Tiddley om pom pom, tiddley om pom pom,
Is what you have to sing.
Tiddley om pom pom, tiddley om pom pom,
Who knows what it may bring?
If you sing it loud enough it can do anything.
Tiddley om pom pom, tiddley om pom pom.
Pom pom is what you sing.

2. If you have wolves and creatures right on your trail,
   If you are lost and feeling grim,
   Just turn and face them with a smile in your heart,
   Soon they will all be joining in.

Refrain Tiddley om pom pom . . .

3. *(dance only — no singing)*

Refrain Tiddley om pom pom . . .

4. If you are miserable, grumpy and sad,
   Just because things are going wrong,
   You have to smile a little through all the rain
   And try a happy little song.

Refrain Tiddley om pom pom . . .   }   *twice*

End of scene 1

SCENE 2   IN THE WOODS

Red Riding Hood   Syble, Syble, where are you?
Come out Syble *please* do!
I've got a little job for us.
It will be fun with two.

Syble   Here ~~I am~~ *we are* Red Riding Hood,
It's really as I feared.
I hid some acorns here last year
And now they've disappeared.

Red Riding Hood   You do this every year, you silly!
Sometimes I do despair.
Mummy's got a freezer you know,
We could keep them safe in there.

Syble   Frozen acorns, yuk! yuk! yuk!
I don't think that would do.
Anyway if I know your mother,
She'd have them in the stew.

Red Riding Hood   Just a minute; over there,
Stand here, take a look.
Isn't that William, what's he doing?
I think he's reading a book!

Syble   Typical! Calls himself a wolf
He hasn't got a clue.
Never done any wolfing in his life.
Look, I know what we'll do.

Red Riding Hood   Now Syble!

Syble   Boo!

William   Oh dear, oh mercy, what a fright.
Oh Syble that's not fair,
Creeping up on a chap like that
And giving him a scare.

I've gone and lost my page now.

8

Red Riding Hood	William, you're a wolf, you clot. You're a ferocious animal, you. You should be stalking deer and such, Not "reading" PICTURES FROM THE ZOO!
William	I knew you were there all the time. My sense of smell, you know.
Red Riding Hood	*and Gyble's* That's no big deal, with Syble's feet — The ~~pong~~'s in everyone's nose. *smell 's*
Syble *& Gyble*	Charming!
William	I'm not cut out for being a wolf That's what my family say. I'm not your predator type really I'm more for running away.

3.   I DON'T WANT TO BE THE BAD WOLF ANY MORE

Solo 1. I'm a round peg in a hole that's square.
          I don't wear the clothes I ought to wear.
All   This is something he's not cut out for,
Solo   And I don't want to be the bad wolf any more.

All   2. In the stories he's the one that's bad.
          No one seems to care when he gets sad.
          This is something he's not cut out for,
Solo   And I don't want to be the bad wolf any more.

All   3. Every time you read a fairy story
          No one ever tells you that he's nice.
          He has never won your hearts or glory.
          He is just the one who ends up sliced!

All   4. Let us put the record straight for you,
          He is just a simple chap like you.
          This is something he's not cut out for,
Solo   And I don't want to be the bad wolf any more.

Solo 5. Every time you read a fairy story
          No one ever tells you that I'm nice.
          I have never won your hearts or glory.
          I am just the one who ends up sliced!

All   6. Let us put the record straight for you,
          He is just a simple chap like you.
          This is something he's not cut out for,
Solo   And I don't want to be the bad wolf any more.

9

William	I just don't frighten anyone. I'm really not a scary 'un. *one*
Red Riding Hood	Well, how do you go on for meals and things?
William	Oh well, you see I'm vegetarian.
Red Riding Hood and All	Vegetarian!
William	Oh yes, vegan, actually. I get by quite well on nuts you know. Why, I found a huge store of acorns Just here, about a week ago.
Syble	Acorns! Nuts! You didn't! I mean! Well really, that's the limit. You save up hard to build a store, Then a wolf gets his snout right in it.
Red Riding Hood	Now don't bicker *argue* you two, I think that's sweet Our William's a real beaut! I think he's fluffy and all squidgy . . .
Syble	Oh no! I think she's going to call *you* cute.
Red Riding Hood	Anyway I'm on an errand. You can come along if you like. I'm going to visit Granny Hood, But I know it's a bit of a hike.
William	Granny Hood, out at Gingerbread Cottage?
Red Riding Hood	Yes.
Syble	The one with the big black cat?
Red Riding Hood	Yes.
William	The one who's got warts and things?
Red Riding Hood	Well, spots really.
Syble	The one with the pointy hat?
Red Riding Hood	Look, if you're thinking she's a witch . . .

William and Syble	No, no, no. Not us!
Red Riding Hood	Daddy says it isn't true. So why make all this fuss?
Syble	Well, I've got some acorns to count. You know, sort by size and weight.
William	And I've got to pick some celery *carrots* And other things to eat.
Syble	Sorry, love to stay and visit Gran But heavens, it's getting late. (*Exits*)
William	*cake* And I've to go and bake a quiche. I haven't time to wait. (*Exits*)
Red Riding Hood	Cowards, I shall just have to go alone. *(Exits)*

Enter Knuckler and Fingers, two robbers, stepping in time to **VILLAINS' MUSIC**

Knuckler	*work* Well Fingers, easy pickings Here, in a little wood. A little old lady's cottage, perhaps Should do us villains good?
Fingers	Yes, Knuckler, a bit of villainy, *steal* We can nick her coat and bag. I likes a little mugging And running off with the swag.
Knuckler	No, no Fingers, burglary Is what I have in mind. Something a little more professional, To be really worth our time.
Fingers	Cor, you're a bad 'un, Knuckler, A real professional you. 'Oo we going to burgle then? 'Oo we going to do?
Knuckler	Wait a minute Fingers, I thinks I hears a sound. Let's hide behind this tree, And see what's to be found.

Red Riding Hood

It's ~~It~~ really ~~is too~~ bad of Syble *& Gyble*
And soft old William, ~~to boot.~~ *too*
I think they're just cowardy custards
And not ~~at all quite~~ cute! *at all*
very

Knuckler

Well now, little girl
Where might you be ~~off?~~ *going?*

Fingers

With this nice red riding hood
And basket full of ~~scoff?~~ *food?*

Red Riding Hood

I'm off to visit my grandmama
Who lives alone, you see.
I'm taking her a flask of stew
So she can have her tea.

Knuckler

Lives alone! The poor old dear,
And did you say down there?

Red Riding Hood

Yes, you can't mistake her,
With her shawl and silvery hair.

Knuckler

She must be grateful for a child
Who looks after her like that?

Fingers

Has she any valuables? Jewellery?
(Knuckler stamps on his foot)
Ow! Why did you do that?

Knuckler

Excuse my friend's bad manners dear.
Please don't disapprove.
You see, when he was only three
He had his brain surgically removed.

Red Riding Hood

Well I must not stop or else this stew
Will be quite thick and cold,
And Granny in a mood about food
Is something to behold.

Knuckler

Well, off you go then, don't mind us.

Fingers

Yes we're simple, humble, burglars . .
(Knuckler stamps on his foot)
OW!!

Knuckler

Buglers, my friend meant, buglers.
For princes and such like that.

Red Riding Hood	~~Oh, there aren't any princes round here.~~ *Goodbye*
~~**Fingers**~~	~~There aren't?~~
~~**Red Riding Hood**~~	No, Granny saw to that!

(Exits)

Knuckler	Now Fingers, if we gets a move on We can do a bit of robbing.
Fingers	Get a move on! With my foot? It's all pink and sore and throbbing.
Knuckler	Oh come on!

4. TRYING TO MAKE CRIME PAY

Knuckler and Fingers	1.	Some ~~chaps~~ *men* go out plumbing, They're fitting joints and pipes. Some go digging roads up For they're just the outdoor type. We work on the night shift We're rarely seen by day. Every night you'll find us busy Trying to make crime pay.
All *Refrain*		In they sneak, up they creep, Filling a big black bag. Then they tiptoe through the window, Off with the swag.
Knuckler and Fingers	2.	Watching for the ~~Bobby~~ *Policeman* As on his beat he pounds. Every occupation has to Have its ups and downs. Still we wouldn't want it To be any other way. Every night you'll find us busy Trying to make crime pay.
All *Refrain*		In they sneak . . .
Knuckler	3.	Join the real professionals. The holidays are fine.
Fingers		Far away as ~~Dartmoor prison~~ *Abashiri* Five years at a time.
Knuckler and Fingers		If somebody asks you We went the other way. Going out about our business Trying to make crime pay.
All		Trying to make crime pay.

Narrator 1

Shawna & Andrea 6
4M

Non-choir

Red

So young unwitting Riding Hood
Had ~~grassed~~ *told* on poor old gran.
And left her to the mercy of
Knuckler and Fingers McMahan. *poor gran*

Mayuka & Lina 3K 7

Non-choir

Houses they liked to burgle,
Old ladies they liked to ~~nobble,~~ *try*
Who even now, are Granny-bound
As fast as Fingers could ~~hobble.~~ *tie*

Narrator 2

Kana & Riri 3K. 8

Non-choir

So what has fate in store for them
Their thoughts so dark and bleak?
As with ill-intent and evil-eyes
Their wicked way, they sneak.

End of Scene 2

SCENE 3 GRANNY'S COTTAGE

VILLAINS' MUSIC

Knuckler

Here we are Fingers, Gingerbread Cottage,
This will be a doddle.
I'll just effect our entry here —
Make sure you use your noddle.
(He knocks)

Granny

Who is it? Go away,
I promise ~~I ain't buying.~~ *I'm not buying*
Whatever it is you're selling,
There's ~~ain't~~ no use ~~you~~ *in* trying.

Knuckler

No, no, madam, let us in.
It's from the council we've been sent.

Granny

From the council, did you say?
What ever's up? I've paid the rent.

Fingers

It's not about the rent my dear,
We've come inspecting roof and floor.
You seem to be infringing
Paragraph 2, Section 8, Clause 184.

14

Granny	Pardon? What are you on about? I don't know what you mean. And you're the strangest council men That I have ever seen.
Knuckler	It's about this cottage For instance, this extension. Did you use Building Regulations?
Fingers	Have you got Planning Permission?
Granny	Eh! What are you on about?
Fingers	The guttering's made of candy — You can't have edible drains!
Granny	But this is a pantomime forest, It never flipping rains. *ever*
Knuckler	And this lintel, it's made of sugar rock — I can break it off and chew it.
Fingers	Look, it's even got 'A Present from Blackpool' Printed all the way through it.
Granny	But it's a gingerbread cottage! It's built like that you nit. *twit* The whole point of a candy house Is you can eat it, bit by bit.
Knuckler	It's really most irregular. Where would these things end? I'm sorry dear, it just won't do, It'll have to be condemned.
Fingers	It's a fire hazard too, you know. Look at that chimney, boss!
Granny	That's not smoke, I have no fire — It's coffee candy floss!
Knuckler	We don't make the rules my dear. You have to have permission Made out on forms in triplicate To the Magic Forestry Commission.

Granny
But it's my home, I'm poor and all alone,
You pair of council twits.
How am I to ~~ensnare~~ catch little kids
If my walls don't have sugary bits?

Knuckler
More than my job's worth, I'm afraid,
We'll have to rope it off.

Fingers
The whole thing isn't safe at all
You'd only have to cough.

Knuckler
Mr Fingers, get the rope.

Narrator 1
And so the two villains,
Protest as Granny might,
Pounced on Granny fast as fast
And tied her up real tight.

Nazneem & Nadia 9
36
Non-choir

Music for TYING UP OF GRANNY

Narrator 2
put
They ~~bundled~~ Granny in the cellar
And bound her with a gag,
And started at the burglaring.

Misha 36 10
choir

Knuckler
Come on now Fingers, swag!

(Knuckler starts filling a bag while Fingers looks around)

Fingers
Knuckler!

Knuckler
What?

Fingers
Do you notice
Something a little strange?
That cauldron, for instance
Instead of a kitchen range.

Knuckler
What do you mean now, Fingers?

Fingers
It's probably nothing, just that
All the hats on the hatstand
Are rather pointed and black.

Knuckler	I know what you mean, that broomstick for instance The one over there on its own. Is what you might call traditional.
Fingers	The sort that a witch might own.
Knuckler & Fingers	A witch!
Knuckler	You tied her up!
Fingers	I didn't. It was your idea!
Knuckler	You put her in the cellar!
Fingers	You hit her with the frying pan!
Knuckler	Oh no! I did, didn't I?
Knuckler	We could let her out, apologise Say we ~~was~~ *were* just having fun.
Fingers	Alternatively we could do the usual —
Knuckler	I quite agree Fingers,
Knuckler & Fingers	Run!!!

Repeat of **TYING UP OF GRANNY MUSIC** *as robbers make a bungling exit*

Narrator 1	*Rei 4P* *Choir* So off through the forest they ~~scarpered~~, *ran* Not knowing ~~their straits were quite dire~~. *what lay in store*
Narrator 2	They were about to leap from the cauldron, Quite accurately into the fire.

Repeat **SONG 2 TIDDLEY OM POM POM**

(lyrics on page 7)

End of scene 3

SCENE 4   IN THE WOODS

VILLAINS' MUSIC

Narrator 1 *Lilian 4M Choir* 12
Now here are two new little fellows,
Whose future our plot will determine.
Mr. BB Wolf and Foxy,
More your traditional vermin.

Narrator 2
Kendra & Maria 3K 3 Choir
They'd moved from their previous location
For the neighbours were not to their taste:
They were often a little bit chewy
So they thought they would try a new place.

BB Wolf
This looks alright, Foxy, nice and dry
I'm sure this forest will do.
I hope we meet some of the neighbours
I'm feeling quite ~~peckish~~ *hungry*. Are you?

Foxy
Yes boss.

BB Wolf
A squirrel perhaps or a rabbit?
My lips I am already licking.
Perhaps I can find you a hen
Or a nice little fattened-up chicken.

Foxy
Yes boss, I think someone's coming
I hear footsteps and someone I see.

BB Wolf
I believe it's a little girl.
Now hide while I catch us our tea.

Foxy
Yes boss.

BB Wolf
I think I'll just stick to roaring,
Something ~~primeval~~ *loud* and wild.
I'll frighten her to death on the spot.
It usually works with a child.

(Red Riding Hood enters)

BB Wolf
ROAR!!!

Red Riding Hood
(mistaking BB Wolf for William)
Hello William. It's no good
I'm quite cross, you're a naughty wolf,
Leaving me like that.

18

BB Wolf	ROAR!!!
Red Riding Hood	And you can stop that, Making a fuss.
BB Wolf	No. Listen. I said ROAR!!!!
Red Riding Hood	I'll "roar" you in a minute. Now I haven't time to waste, Be off with you or I'll smack you.
BB Wolf	You'll what? I mean, ROAR!!!!
Red Riding Hood	Don't come running to me when You're frightened. I'm off, I'm busy. *(Exits)*
BB Wolf	Frightened! Running! What's going on Is everybody mad? I'm a wolf, for heavens sake I'm seriously quite bad.
Foxy	What happened boss? Where's dinner?
BB Wolf	Dunno! I haven't got a clue. That was first class roaring that was. What more have I got to do?
Foxy	There's someone else boss.
BB Wolf	Right! I'm angry now, watch this.

(Knuckler and Fingers come running in.)

BB Wolf	~~Halt!~~ Stop! Wait right there. I'm a wolf and therefore rather nasty, And I'm going to have you for my lunch And serve you up in a pasty. ROAR!!!!
Knuckler	Just a minute.
BB Wolf	Pardon?
Knuckler	May I consult with my colleague?
BB Wolf	Sorry?
Knuckler	You know, have a ~~chinwag~~ talk.

BB Wolf	I suppose so, but it's most irregular.
Knuckler *(to Fingers)*	That way, is a witch Who's probably in a mood,
Fingers	And that way, is a wolf Who rather thinks we're food.
Knuckler	A witch can do quite horrible things. That makes me feel quite sick.
Fingers	And it can last forever and ever . . .
Knuckler	At least with a wolf it's quick!
Fingers	That's agreed then.
Knuckler	That's agreed. Right Mr Wolf, how do you want us?
BB Wolf	Pardon?
Knuckler	Grilled, boiled or fried?
Fingers	Baked might be nice you know. Nicely crisp on the outside.
BB Wolf	Er, I hadn't really thought . . . Aren't you frightened?
Knuckler	Oh yes.
Fingers	But not of you, you see.
Knuckler	Hurry up, make your mind up. ~~Fricasséed?~~ Lightly toasted? Baked
Fingers	How about sautéed in white wine sauce Or maybe gently roasted?
Knuckler	rib Do you want a leg, a ~~haunch~~? For heaven's sake decide.

Fingers	What about in a sesame bun, With a little salad on the side?
BB Wolf	I don't know, I'm all confused. As much as I like killing, It rather takes the fun away When dinner is eager and willing.
Knuckler	Don't take too long. I warn you That we haven't time to waste. I cannot guarantee we'll be Entirely to your taste.
BB Wolf	I don't know, I really don't, It just does not seem right. I like my lunch to struggle a bit. I've lost my appetite.
Knuckler	Right, we're off, perhaps we'll pinch A carriage for a start, And then we're getting out of here . . .
Fingers	They call it "a la carte". *(They exit)*
Foxy	What's going on boss? That is twice You've failed to get our dinner. I'm getting very hungry And I'm sure I'm inches thinner.
BB Wolf	Hang on, there's someone else. Quick, hide! Oh! It's another wolf.

(Enter William and Syble) & Syble

BB Wolf	Hello there friend. It's good to see Another ~~canine too~~ wolf like you I'm BB Wolf, I've just moved in. May I say, how do you do?
William	Pleased to meet you and your friend, I hope you're happy here. It's rather quiet and dull you know Not much fun, I fear.

BB Wolf It's rather strange, I do admit,
No one seems much scared,
Of wolves I mean. I've roared and roared,
My fangs I've even bared.

William Oh we don't do things like that round here,
You'll want the wood next door.
They've got wolves and trolls and things
And dragons by the score.

Everybody's friendly here,
It's really for the best.
We don't have people round for tea
Then go and eat the guest.

BB Wolf Well things are going to change round here
On that you can bet.
Us wolves are not exactly
Famous for our etiquette.

Come on Foxy, we'll start with that
Little girl with the red hood.

Foxy Yes Boss.

(They exit)

Syble I think that this means trouble.
~~What are we to do?~~ Don't you agree
Red Riding Hood's in trouble
And she's only got us ~~two.~~ three.

William Come on, we'll get the Woodman
Tell ~~Acquaint~~ him with all the facts.
Then we'll find the Big Bad Wolf
And explain things, with his axe!

Syble Good idea. CHOIR
Turaluralu

All Good idea.

(They exit)

✱ 2S dancers on stage
2S instrumentalists stand up

22

5.   **TURALURALU**

(All sing with action/dance routine)

1.   When you're all on your own and you've nowhere to go,
     And the night seems so cold and so long.
     When the shadows are dancing and darkness is there,
     In the distance you'll hear this small song.

Refrain   Turalura-turalu it sings,
            Turalura-lura-lay.
            Turalura-turalu it sings,
            Turalura-lura-lay.

2.   If there's no one to help you or guide you away,
     If you haven't a thing going right.
     Take a small piece of silence and treasure it well.
     You will hear in the deep of the night . . .

Refrain   Turalura-turalu it sings . . .

End of scene 4

SCENE 5   WOODMAN'S COTTAGE

Woodman   This stew's nice dear, what's in it?
                Is it cabbages or leek?

Mother   Dunno, I've quite forgotten,
                It's been boiling for a week.

Woodman   Where's our little Red Riding Hood?
                She's been gone a while.
                She ought to be back home by now,
                It's only a couple of miles.

Mother   Dawdling, I expect, or playing
                With those friends of hers,
                That Italian lad . . .

Woodman   Oh, Pinocchio.

Mother   Or one of those three bears.

(Enter William and Syble)
       & Gyble

William   Oh Woodman, Woodman, there's a wolf *here*
                        Abroad, tell us what we do.

                        Well, you're a wolf
Mother   ~~Well if he's abroad it doesn't matter does it?~~
                        Why does it worry you?

                        ~~Anyway, you're a wolf!~~

Syble   No, this is a wolf with a capital Woh.
                        You know, the nasty sort.
                        Not like William. One that bites
                        And knows how to roar and snort.

William   A hungry wolf, a big bad wolf,
                        Not a wolf like me.
                        One that's got a temper and he
                        Hasn't had his tea!

Mother   Red Riding Hood, she's all alone
                        We've got to go and stop her.
                        If the wolf should find her
                        He'll probably go and ~~scoff~~ her.
                                  eat

William   I should have fought him in a fight
                        Although I know he'd beat me.
                        I'm not a proper wolf you see,
                        I've a lot of poodle in me.

Syble   Don't blame yourself, it's not your fault
                        As a wolf you're sleek and tall,
                        Strong fangs, good roar and bushy tail.
                        You're just a bit soft, that's all.

Woodman   Right, I'll get my axe and we'll be off.
                        A wolf eh? We'll soon see.
                        Come on, let's hurry on our way.

Syble and William	Did somebody say 'we'?

Woodman	Yes, come on you ~~two.~~ *three* I'll need your help, Someone I can trust. Or will you leave her to her fate?

Syble and William	Alright then, if we must.

Woodman	Come along.

End of scene 5

SCENE 6 IN THE WOODS

Narrator 1 *Luna 3K* *choir* 14	So off they went as quick as quick To rescue Riding Hood. Meanwhile our robbers they were wandering Lost deep in the wood.

(Enter Knuckler and Fingers stepping in time to **VILLAINS' MUSIC***)*

Shayan 3K *choir* 15	Truth to tell, as robbers went These two were pretty poor. Still, at least on this occasion, They'd kept the wolf from the door!

Narrator 2 *Ben 3K* *choir* 16	A life of crime just does not pay They'd found out to their cost. So here they are, tired and wet, Very fed up, and . . .

Knuckler	Lost! We're lost, we're lost, we're going to starve.

Fingers	Just a minute, Knuckler, someone's coming.

(Enter Woodman, William and Syble)
& Syble

Knuckler	Thank goodness, I'm really pleased We were completely lost. And now we've come across you chaps, *four* I'm glad our paths have crossed.
Woodman	Have you seen a little girl?
Fingers	In a red cape?
Knuckler	Has a granny?
Fingers	Silver haired, lives in a cottage?
Knuckler	Taking her a basket?
William	Yes that's her.
Fingers	Nope, not seen *any* ~~no~~-one like that.
William	Well, how do you know she's got a granny and is taking her a basket?
Knuckler	Good question that.
Fingers	Yes, glad you asked it.
Knuckler	Alright it's a fair ~~cop~~ *question* You've caught us out I fear. I'll confess to everything Just get us out of here.
Fingers	We *were* ~~was~~ only doing a little burglaring You know, it's just a hobby — Break into an old dear's house And empty out her lobby.
Knuckler	Only she was a witch, we didn't know She must have been in disguise. It was after we threw her in the cellar That we then realised.

Syble and All	Threw Granny Hood in the cellar? Oh no, she will be fumin' I wouldn't like to be you two, It's a wonder you're still human.
William	I wouldn't like to be in your shoes Or more probably hooves. She's got some nasty spells for people Of whom she disapproves.
Knuckler & Fingers	Oh no, what we going to do?
Woodman	You'd better come and help us We're after a wolf, you see. She might look on more kindly, If I say you assisted me.
Knuckler	Right, that's it, we're going straight! Our duty we'll not shirk. Tell me, this spell, the nasty one, Does it always work?
William	Always!
Fingers & Knuckler	Oh no!!! *(They all exit)*

End of scene 6

SCENE 7   GRANNY'S COTTAGE

Repeat of **TYING UP OF GRANNY MUSIC**

Narrator 1 ₃₆ Maria & Layla	7 And so our heroes headed For granny's little hovel. The Woodman, to rescue Riding Hood, The robbers to try and grovel.
choir	
Saki 36	18 Meanwhile the wicked, nasty wolf Had streaked ahead like lightning. He'd got inside the cottage And was practising being frightening.
choir	

27

Narrator 2

Arya 36 19
choir

He knew Miss Hood would be going there
It wasn't just plain luck,
It was traditional in pantomimes.
And anyway, he'd read the book.

BB Wolf

Well here I am, Gingerbread House,
And soon I'll be fed and fat.
Lunch delivered right to the door,
~~I could call it 'dial-a-brat'.~~
How wonderful, fancy that.

Granny

Mm . . . mm . . . . . mm . . . .

BB Wolf

What's that noise? I'm imagining things.
It gave me quite a fright.
It must be lack of protein
Still, I'll soon get that put right.

Now let me see . . .

VILLAINS' MUSIC

(He puts on Granny's cap, shawl and glasses and sits in a rocking chair).

BB Wolf

I suppose we'll have the
'What big eyes you have' routine.
Honestly, what a nerve!
Still, I suppose it's traditional,
A bit like having an hors d'oeuvre.

or

(Red Riding Hood arrives and knocks)

BB Wolf

Come in dinner . . . . . I mean dear.

Red Riding Hood

Hello Gran, I've brought you
A basket of food, and some other goodies.

BB Wolf

Come a bit closer dear,
Then I can eat you, er see you, I mean.

Red Riding Hood

My, Granny, what big eyes you have!

BB Wolf

All the better to see you with my dear.

Red Riding Hood

And what big ears you have, Granny!

BB Wolf	All the better to hear you with my dear.
Red Riding Hood	And what a big nose you have, Granny!
BB Wolf	Well, it's not *that* big you know, but big enough I suppose.
Red Riding Hood	And what big feet you have, Granny!
BB Wolf	Aren't we getting a bit personal here, my dear? They're only size 9's after all.
Red Riding Hood	In fact, you look exactly like a big . . . .
BB Wolf	Yes?
Red Riding Hood	Bad . . .
BB Wolf	Yes?
Red Riding Hood	Nasty . . .
BB Wolf	Yes?
Red Riding Hood	Wolf.
BB Wolf	Got it in one!
Red Riding Hood	Oh no!

(The Woodman, Robbers, William and Syble come running in)

All	There he is.
Woodman	Let me at him.
BB Wolf	Drat! I forgot about this bit.
Red Riding Hood	If you're going to be a wolf And eat up all your friends, Remember, when you read a fairy tale, Read right up to the end.

(Granny appears)

Granny	What's going on?
All	Granny!
Granny	First I get the council Trying to demolish my lovely home. Then I'm trussed up like a chicken And in my cellar thrown. I'm MAD, do you hear me? MAD!!
All	Yes Granny.
Granny	*Very* mad!
All	Yes Granny.
Granny	And when I'm mad I'm really mad, Mad with a capital 'M'. Where's them council officials? I know what to do with them.
Knuckler	We're really sorry Granny, You should be cross, you ought. We'd really never have done it . . .
Fingers	Not if we'd known we'd get caught.
Granny	And who's this?
Syble	The Big Bad Wolf.
Granny	So you're bad, are you?
BB Wolf	Just a little bit.
Granny	And you were going to eat my granddaughter?
BB Wolf	Good heavens no! Not all of her Just a leg perhaps, a bit of an arm.

Woodman
Let me at him, hold my coat,
I'll show that Wolf who's who.
I'll take my trusty axe and
I'll chop him into two.

Granny
I'll deal with this, these ~~reprobates~~, villains
I'll ~~magic~~ 'em, you'll see!   cast a spell
And they will wish they'd never tried
To put one over me.

Sounds to represent the spell

Granny
This is the spell of Granny Hood —
From now, henceforth, you will be 'good'.   } *Repeated by All*

BB Wolf
Oh no, not 'good', anything but 'good'.

Knuckler
But we're villains!

Fingers
It's our livelihood.

BB Wolf
I'll end up carrying slippers,
Begging, doing tricks.
I've suddenly got this urge
To wag my tail and fetch a stick.

William
Here, let's try it *(throws a stick)*
Go on, fetch.

BB Wolf
Woof! *(like a doggie. Exits)*

Granny
(to robbers)
And you two, you're forgiven.
It's no use standing muttering.
Now go and get a ladder,
You can start by clearing my guttering.

Knuckler & Fingers   Yes Granny.

(They exit)

Narrator 1	And so our tale is over
Peter & Nick *20*	We hope you've all had fun.
36 choir	And now our cast would like to say
	'Goodbye' to everyone.

Actors/actresses say this:

Narrator 2	We suggest you all leave quickly
(pointing to audience)	We would if we were you,
	Before our granny wants her tea
	And finds out that it's 'stew'.

| Granny | It's stew !!****** |
| *(opening flask)* | |

FINALE

6. IT'S THAT KIND OF CHRISTMAS TIME OF THE YEAR

(All with action/dance routine. All the cast are involved)

1. In the steeple bells are ringing and birds are winging away.
    In the fields the winds are blowing, they'll soon be going away.
    In and out of chimneys Santa's sleigh will have to steer.
    It's that kind of Christmas time of the year.

2. In the houses fires are burning and rain is turning to snow.
    At the North Pole Santa's loading and getting ready to go.
    Hang your stockings by the bed and give a little cheer.
    It's that kind of Christmas time of the year.

3. It seems just a moment when summer lay round,
    Now it's frost and snowdrops that are laying on the ground.

4. On the lakes there're people skating and some folk waiting to play.
    By the fire the kettle's steaming and father's dreaming away.
    Children looking out for Father Christmas's reindeer.
    It's that kind of Christmas time of the,
        It's that kind of Christmas time of the,
        It's that kind of Christmas time of the year.

(bows and exits taken to repeat of music)

THE END

ISBN 0-7119-5027-X

Printed and bound in Great Britain by
Caligraving Limited Thetford Norfolk

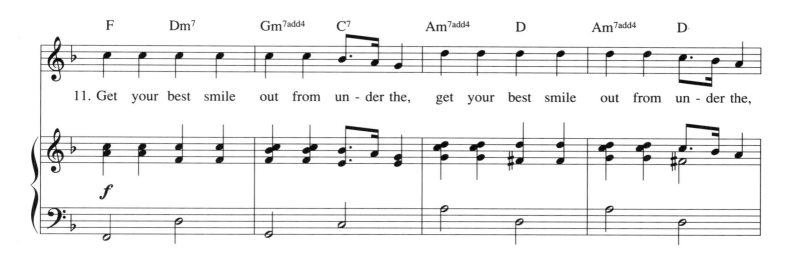

11. Get your best smile out from un - der the, get your best smile out from un - der the,

get your best smile out from un - der the stair.

2
TIDDLEY OM POM POM

All
Action/dance routine

1. Cue: That girl! (end of scene 1)   *2. Cue: . . . Quite accurately into the fire. (End of scene 3)*

kind of a sound, all of your cares will fly a - way.
smile in your heart, soon they will all be join - ing in.
through all the rain and try a hap - py lit - tle song.

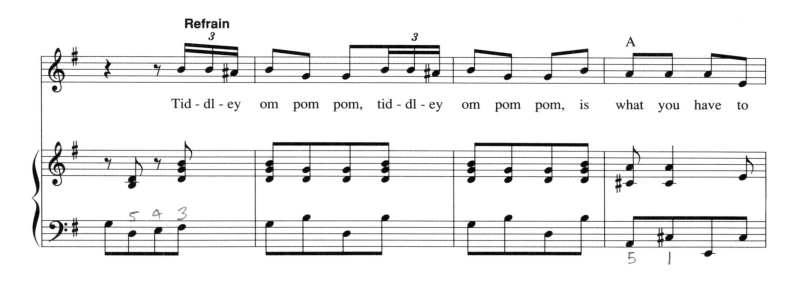

Tid - dl - ey om pom pom, tid - dl - ey om pom pom, is what you have to

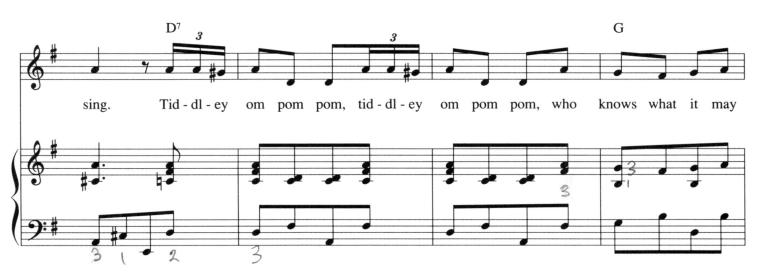

sing. Tid - dl - ey om pom pom, tid - dl - ey om pom pom, who knows what it may

what you have to sing. Tid-dl-ey om pom pom, tid-dl-ey om pom pom, who

knows what it may bring? If you sing it loud e-nough it can do an-y-

-thing. Tid-dl-ey om pom pom, tid-dl-ey om pom pom. Pom pom is what you sing.

3

I DON'T WANT TO BE THE BAD WOLF ANY MORE

William + All

Cue: . . . I'm more for running away.

Solo: 1. I'm a round peg in a hole that's square. I don't wear the clothes I
All: 2. In the sto-ries he's the one that's bad. No one seems to care when

ought to wear. **All:** This is some-thing he's not cut out for, **Solo:** and
he gets sad. This is some-thing he's not cut out for, **Solo:** and

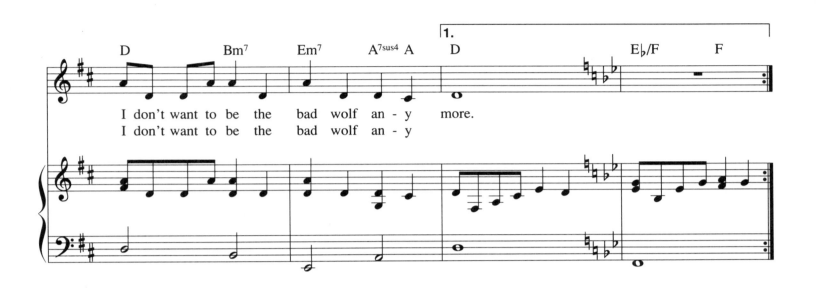

Chords (measures 1–4): D, Bm⁷, Em⁷, A⁷ˢᵘˢ⁴, A, D, E♭/F, F

I don't want to be the bad wolf an-y more.
I don't want to be the bad wolf an-y

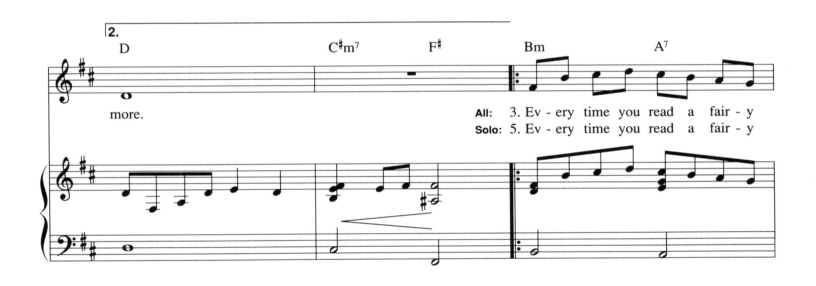

Chords: D, C#m⁷, F#, Bm, A⁷

more.

All: 3. Ev-er-y time you read a fair-y
Solo: 5. Ev-er-y time you read a fair-y

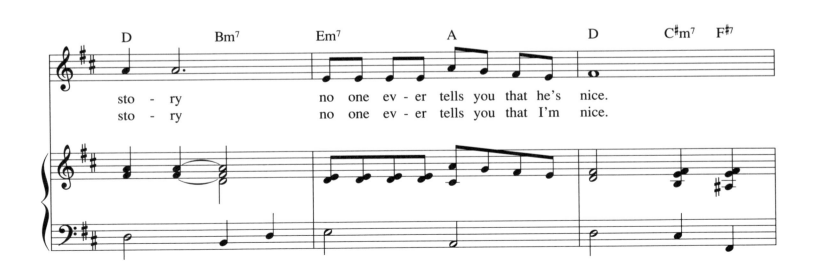

Chords: D, Bm⁷, Em⁷, A, D, C#m⁷, F#⁷

sto - ry no one ev-er tells you that he's nice.
sto - ry no one ev-er tells you that I'm nice.

He has nev - er won your hearts or glo - ry. He is just the one who ends up
I have nev - er won your hearts or glo - ry. I am just the one who ends up

sliced!
sliced!

All: 4. Let us put the rec - ord
All: 6. Let us put the rec - ord

straight for you, he is just a sim - ple chap like you.
straight for you, he is just a sim - ple chap like you.

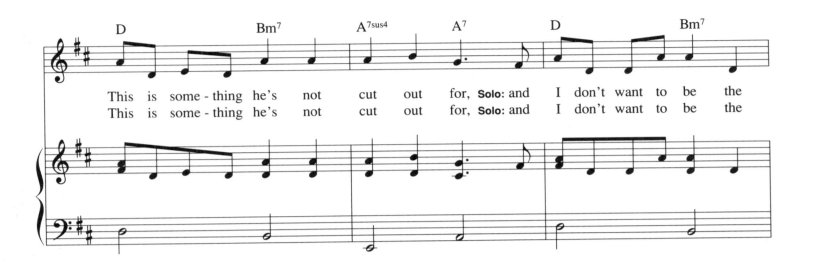

This is some-thing he's not cut out for, **Solo:** and I don't want to be the
This is some-thing he's not cut out for, **Solo:** and I don't want to be the

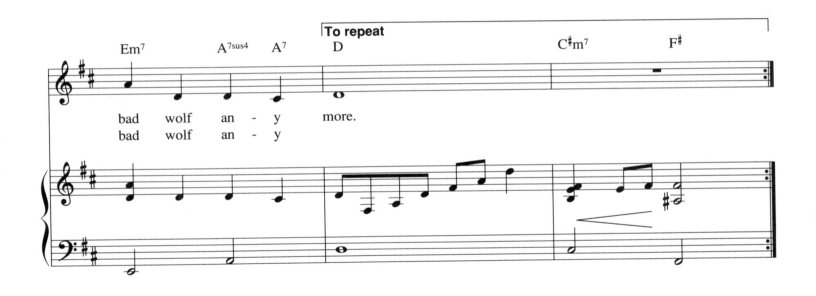

To repeat

bad wolf an - y more.
bad wolf an - y

To finish

more.

diminuendo   *rit.*   **pp**

INCIDENTAL MUSIC FOR VILLAINS

1. Scene 2   Cue: Cowards, I shall just have to go alone.
2. Scene 3   Opening Music
3. Scene 4   Opening Music
4. Scene 6   Cue: . . . Lost deep in the wood.
5. Scene 7   Cue: Now let me see . . .

Spookily ♩ = 121

4
TRYING TO MAKE CRIME PAY

Robbers + All

Cue: Oh come on!

Knuckler and Fingers:

1. Some chaps go out plumb - ing, they're fit - ting joints and pipes. Some go dig - ging roads up for they're just the out - door type. We work on the night shift we're
2. Watch - ing for the Bob - by as on his beat he pounds. Ev - ery oc - cu - pa - tion has to have its ups and downs. Still we would - n't want it to

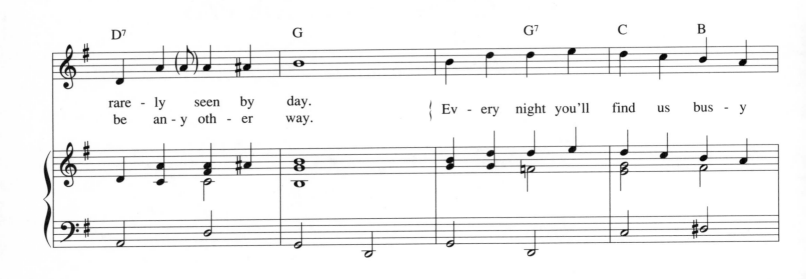

rare - ly seen by day.
be an - y oth - er way.

Ev - ery night you'll find us bus - y

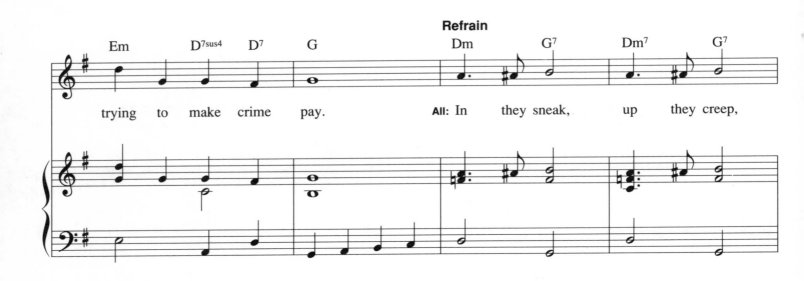

trying to make crime pay.

Refrain

All: In they sneak, up they creep,

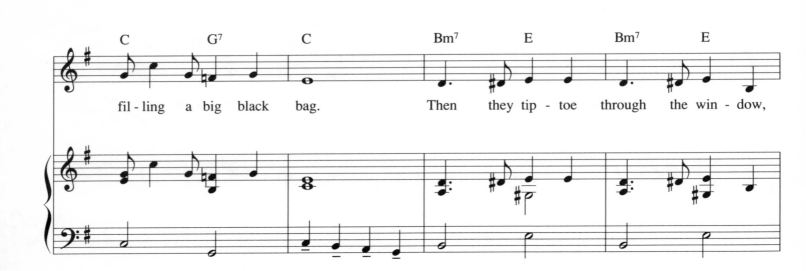

fil - ling a big black bag. Then they tip - toe through the win - dow,

off with the swag. **Knuckler:** 3. Join the real pro - fess - ionals. The

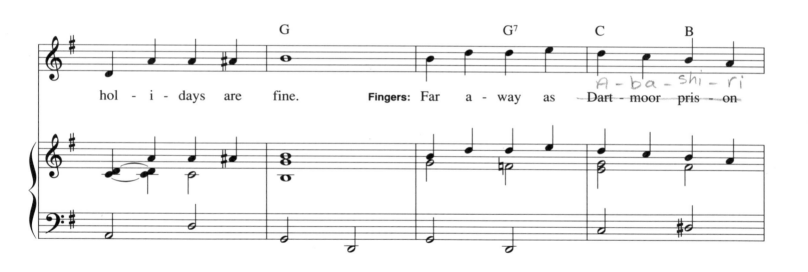

hol - i - days are fine. **Fingers:** Far a - way as Dart - moor pris - on *A - ba - shi - ri*

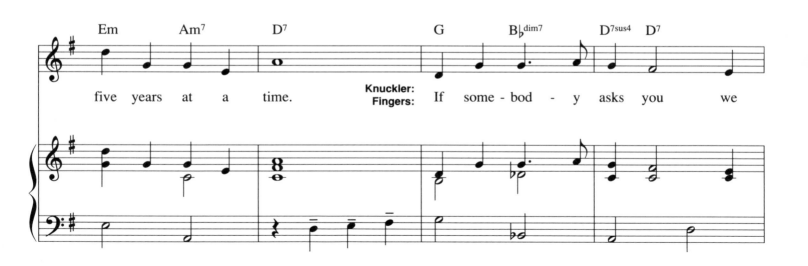

five years at a time. **Knuckler:** **Fingers:** If some - bod - y asks you we

went the oth - er way. Go - ing out a - bout our busi - ness

trying to make crime pay. **All:** Trying to make crime pay.

INCIDENTAL MUSIC FOR TYING UP OF GRANNY

1. Scene 3   *Cue: . . . And tied her up real tight.*   *2.* Scene 3   *Cue: Run!!!*
3. Scene 7   Opening Music.

5
TURALURALU

All
Action/dance routine

Cue: Good idea. Good idea.

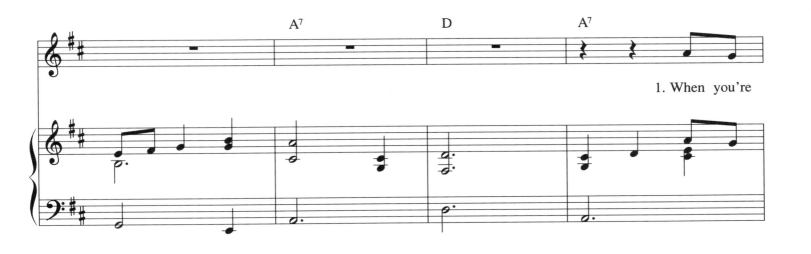

1. When you're

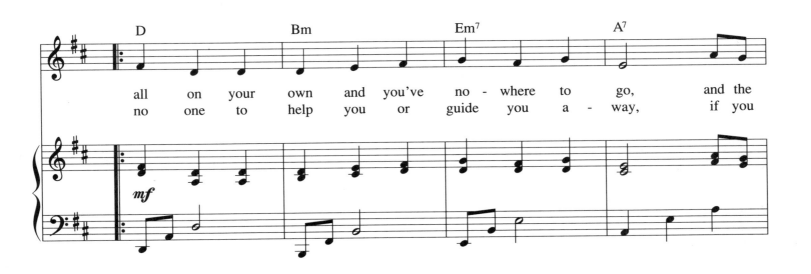

all on your own and you've no - where to go, and the
no one to help you or guide you a - way, if you

night seems so cold and so long. When the
have - n't a thing go - ing right. Take a

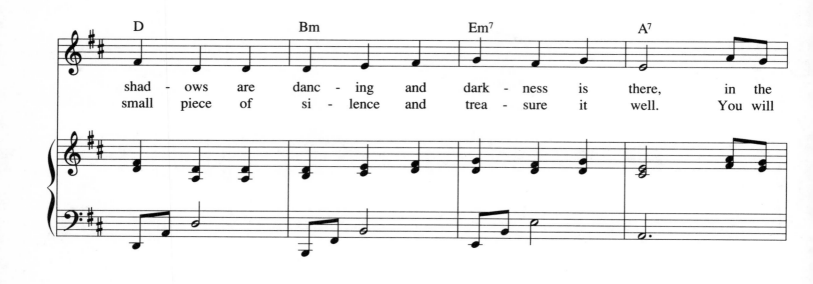

shad - ows are danc - ing and dark - ness is there, in the
small piece of si - lence and trea - sure it well. You will

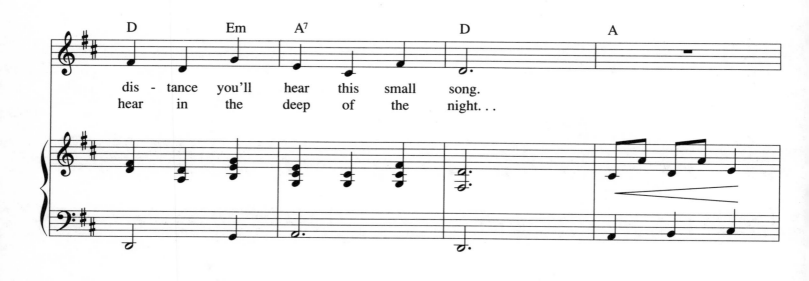

dis - tance you'll hear this small song.
hear in the deep of the night. . .

Refrain

Tu - ra - lu - ra - tu - ra - lu it sings,

28

tu - ra - lu - ra - lu - ra - lay._____

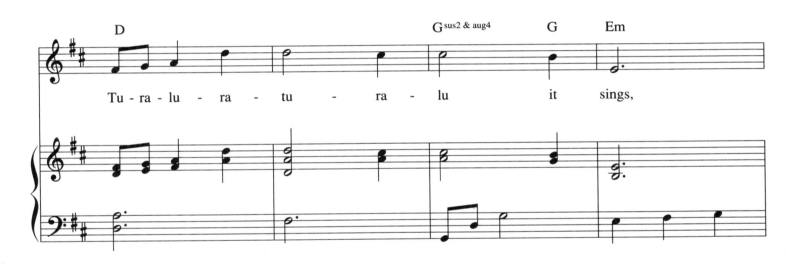

Tu - ra - lu - ra - tu - ra - lu it sings,

tu - ra - lu - ra - lu - ra - lay. 2. If there's -lay.

6
IT'S THAT KIND OF CHRISTMAS TIME OF THE YEAR

All
Action/dance routine

Cue: It's stew!! *****

winds are blow - ing, they'll soon be go - ing a - way. In and out of
San - ta's load - ing and get - ting read - y to go. Hang your stock - ings

chim - neys San - ta's sleigh will have to steer. It's that kind of
by the bed and give a lit - tle cheer.

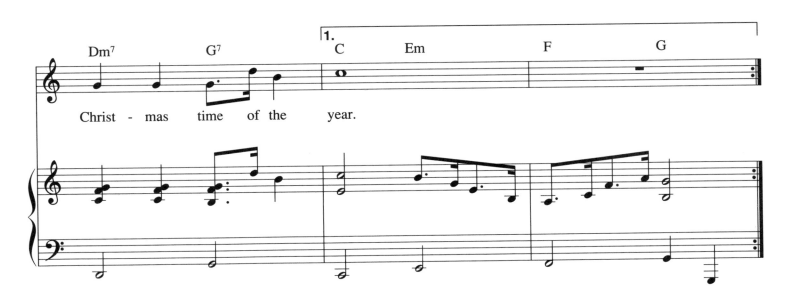

Christ - mas time of the year.

4. On the lakes there're peo - ple skat - ing and some folk wait - ing to play.

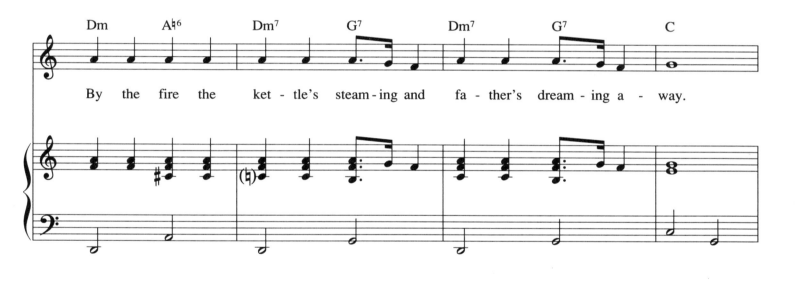

By the fire the ket - tle's steam - ing and fa - ther's dream - ing a - way.

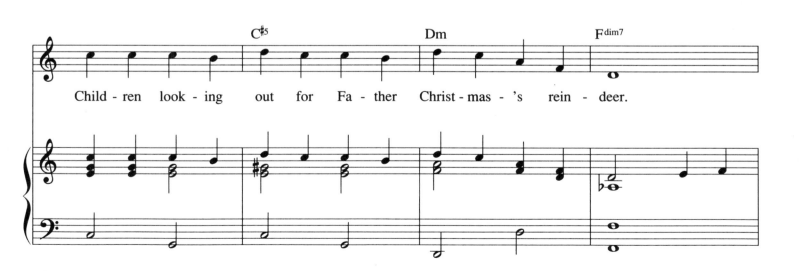

Child - ren look - ing out for Fa - ther Christ - mas - 's rein - deer.

It's that kind of Christ - mas time of the, it's that kind of

Christ - mas time of the, it's that kind of Christ - mas time of the

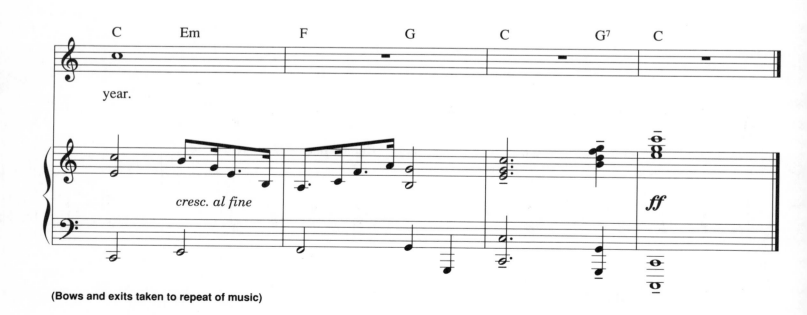

year.

cresc. al fine

ff

(Bows and exits taken to repeat of music)

Printed and bound in Great Britain by
Caligraving Limited Thetford Norfolk

BLANK PAGE FOR TEACHER'S OWN PRODUCTION NOTES

35